This should be it,
Only the best to you -
From now on.
Anna May Johnson

YOU'VE GOT ME
IN STITCHES

Mack   Argosy

"Let's try not to make any mistakes—this is being televised!"

YOU'VE GOT ME
IN STITCHES

Edited by *LAWRENCE LARIAR*

A COLLECTION OF
GAY CARTOONS
ABOUT DOCTORS, PATIENTS
AND HOSPITALS

DODD, MEAD & COMPANY · NEW YORK

Books by Lawrence Lariar

HUMOR

FISH AND BE DAMNED!

BEST CARTOONS OF THE YEAR

OH! DOCTOR KINSEY!

YANKEE YIDDISH

BED AND BORED

EASY WAY TO CARTOONING

CAREERS IN CARTOONING

CARTOONING FOR EVERYBODY

FATHER GOOSENAGLE (WITH COL. STOOPNAGLE)

THE ARMY FUN BOOK

GOLF AND BE DAMNED!

NOVELS

THE MAN WITH THE LUMPY NOSE

THE GIRL WITH THE FRIGHTENED EYES

DEATH PAINTS THE PICTURE

HE DIED LAUGHING

FRIDAY FOR DEATH

YOU CAN'T CATCH ME!

RUN FOR YOUR LIFE

THE DAY I DIED

WIN, PLACE AND DIE

ON SELLING

THE SALESMAN'S TREASURY

LITHOGRAPHED IN THE UNITED STATES OF AMERICA
BY THE MURRAY PRINTING COMPANY, FORGE VILLAGE, MASS.

FOREWORD

ANYBODY WHO thinks there isn't an important reason for a book of this type had best hurry to the nearest hospital for proof. A recent survey of hospitalized patients, taken by the Hospitalized Patients Survey Company, shows a remarkable lack of things to do while waiting for the incisions to heal. A poll of 3,876 patients revealed the following breakdown of their leisure:

1,345 patients admitted they spent all their waking hours gazing vacantly at the ceiling.

856 confessed they stared out of the window looking for birds, planes, blimps, clouds, flying saucers or any other airborne objects.

3,278 said they spent most of their waking hours tuning out radio programs.

3,091 (males) admitted they concentrated their full energies wishing for that pretty blonde nurse to come back and administer an alcohol rub.

Thirty patients had nothing to say at all, mostly because they were either (A) In a coma, (B) In the Contagious Disease Wing and could not be interviewed, or, (C) Not yet out of the ether.

The fact remains that most sick people in hospitals require strong doses of laughter and good cheer. Too often, the ordinary patient is subjected to the ultimate in mental cruelty while waiting for the happy day when he will be dismissed. As soon as the operation proves a success or the disease shows signs of being defeated, the unfortunate convalescent finds himself facing the greatest ordeal of all—the steady flow of well-wishers who come to torment him during visiting hours.

These purveyors of joy and gladness should be carefully screened by a trained psychologist before being allowed to enter any sickroom. Such an analysis might go a long way toward shortening the convalescent period of the patient, since not a few of the guests seem to affect the patient in a negative way, causing sudden loss of breath, bubbling blood pressure, migraine headaches, spots before the eyes, heaves, and hot and cold running depressions.

A lack of space allows only a quick breakdown of the various types of lunatic allowed to enter a hospital room ungagged. Anybody who ever survived their tortures should recognize them at once:

1: *The Cheerful Ghoul* (or *Mournful Moaner*) who tells you about several of his friends who passed into the limbo after exactly the same type of operation you had.

2: *The Silent Sympathiser* (or *Dumb Dunderhead*) who has nothing at all to say, but sits staring at you misty-eyed.

3: *The Noisy Comic* (or *Happy Hooligan*) who lets fly with a barrage of loud jokes, quips and anecdotes he'd never dare tell you if you had your strength and were able to hit him.

4: *The Hungry Hound* (or *Apple Stealer*) who has dropped by only because he wants to ravage your gift candy, fruits and nuts.

5: *The Family Fusspot* (or *Chum Collector*) who has scrupulously combed the country to bring you a cozy covey of relatives you haven't seen for decades and had hoped to avoid for the rest of your life.

This book was conceived as an antidote to all the above well-intentioned charmers. It was created to bring your sick friend the ultimate in enjoyment. The intelligent and thoughtful visitor need only follow a few simple rules to qualify as a welcome guest in any hospital in the land.

Simply go to your nearest bookstore and purchase this book.

Next, lay the volume gently within reach of your sick friend.

And finally, go home.

LAWRENCE LARIAR

Freeport, N. Y.
February, 1954

To
William H. Zinsser
President of the Lenox Hill Hospital,
New York, 1941-1953
who first suggested this book
and invites you to laugh with him over it

Sharp

Liberty

"I've discovered a cure for which there is no known disease!"

Oakes   The Physician

Bo Brown   Collier's

"Now don't you worry about *me!* I've got some of the
girls from the office helping me with the housework."

O'Brien

"Now would you like the kiss you were trying so hard for?"

Sharp

"I said—'that will be ten dollars!'"

Taber

"I brought you a bunch of flowers, Ed, but I er . . .
well, you know how it is . . ."

"Excuse me, but what medical journal is this going to be in?"

Marquez   Collier's

**"Do you by any chance still have some of those pills
I gave you last week? They were a string of beads
my wife wanted restrung!"**

Rayon

**"You just take it easy, dear—and don't say you
never had a vacation."**

Whiting

"It's a moll."

Gibson

Saturday Evening Post

"We just help the nurses—they haven't taught us
operating yet."

**"Has the senator been kissing babies lately?—
It's measles."**

"Congratulations—it's a baby!"

O'Brien   American

"If they come out good, I'll take a half dozen."

Boltinoff

"No, no, Mary! He's waiting to see me!"

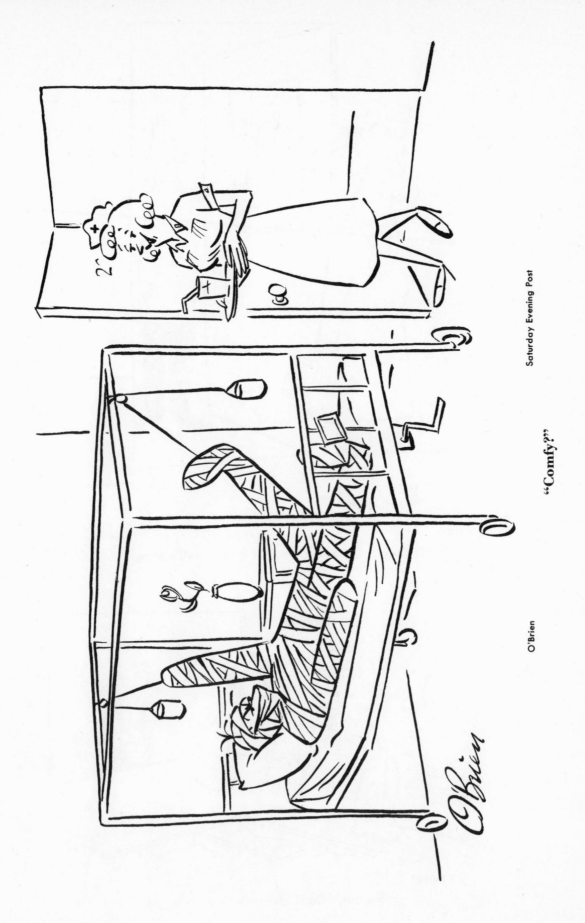

O'Brien

"Comfy?"

Saturday Evening Post

Goldstein   Saturday Evening Post

**"Yours is a common enough personality problem,
Mr. Rankley—you're obnoxious."**

Tyrell

**"*I'm* the beautiful nurse who took care of you when
you were so sick."**

Whiting

"Quite often I have the gnawing feeling that people are ignoring me."

Scott Brown

Collier's

"General Hospital, but don't worry—I'm just going to visit a sick friend."

Millar

"Don't use that injured arm any more than you have to."

"Okay, lady, but from now on you'll have to take
it yourself."

"Now, now—let's just forget our fear of snakes for
a minute."

Sharp

"My wife had to go back to work today!"

McCormick

Saturday Evening Post

"We were just passing, doc, and I decided to drop
in for a checkup."

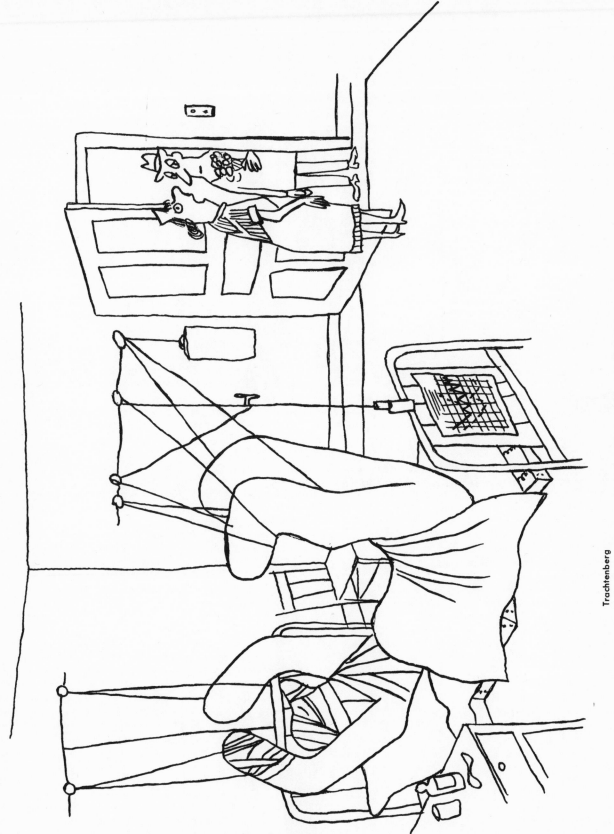

Trachtenberg

"You can't see him now. He's resting."

Price

Saturday Evening Post

"The extra ten dollars, doctor, was because we had to call in an ignition specialist for consultation."

Syverson

Collier's

Boserman

"I made her stay in bed, doctor, but it wasn't easy."

Price   Liberty

"Don't be startled—just one apiece!"

Quinn   American

**"*Imagine!* Telling me I'm in perfect health. How
does a 'quack' like that stay in business?"**

Rodriguez

Saturday Evening Post

"Stumped, eh?"

Roir   Saturday Evening Post

"Had that taken out too, doc—guess again."

Corka   Collier's

"What do I do if the stork comes while you're gone?"

Dempsey   Collier's

"Dad's friends have been swell. They come over and play cards with him every night."

Ketcham   Collier's

"He looks much better today, doctor. Now make sure he keeps his feet covered, gets plenty of sleep, and we'll have him out of here in no time."

Marcus

Saturday Evening Post

"NURSE!"

Boltinoff

Judge

"I take it you came to see me!"

Locke   Collier's

"Nice of you fellows to come see me so often. What's happening in the nurses' quarters now?"

" . . . and I'd lay off this stuff if I were you."

"Pulse, 80; temperature, 103; income, 25,000 net."

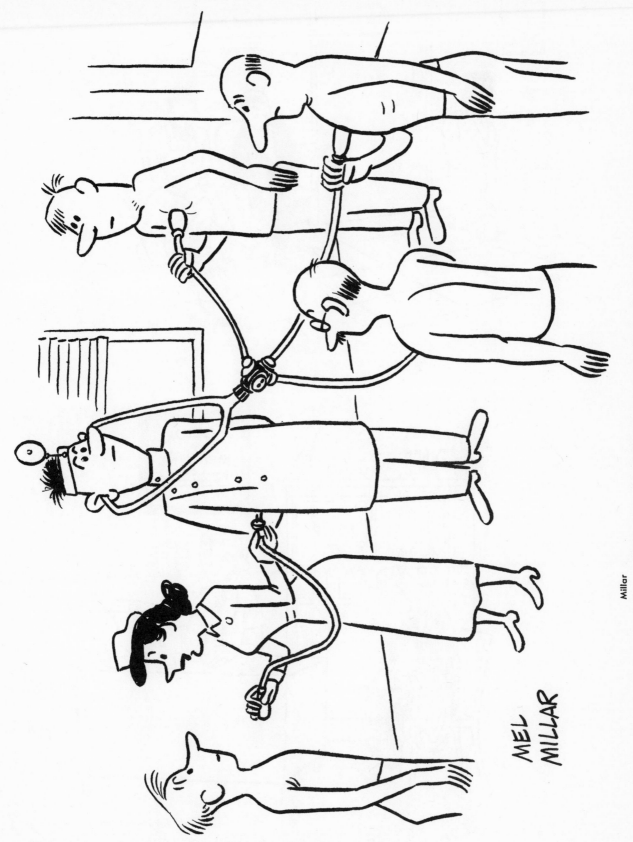

Millar

"Just plug in—the doctor is a very busy man."

MEL MILLAR

Paplow

Collier's

Bernhardt

Saturday Evening Post

"There's really nothing unusual about your condition, Mr. Phlinch, except for the fact that it is so seldom encountered in a person who is still living."

Dennis

Pearson

American

"Miss Locke, I wish you wouldn't refer to hypodermic injections as your needle work."

"About an hour after I eat I get a sharp pain between the Union Jack and the Hawaiian dancer."

"I still don't think this is what the doctor meant by outside interests."

Gibson   Saturday Evening Post

"Dear me, I've been waiting so long I think I've recovered."

La Mendola

"Well, Dr. Browne, I'll be seeing you."

Ridgeway

Saturday Evening Post

"Just how much of a raise did you think I got?"

"Don't say I never gave you nothing!"

**"Take one upon going to bed, and the other if you
wake up in the morning."**

Wolfe   Saturday Evening Post

**"Don't worry about the hospital bills, dear—they're
less than you would spend if you were well!"**

Corka   Saturday Review of Literature

**"Ellery Q. Carr, Hercule P. Carr, Sherlock H. Carr—
why, darling, they'll be a great hit with the boys."**

King

True Detective

**"Edgar came out of the accident pretty luckily, but
I'm suffering from shock."**

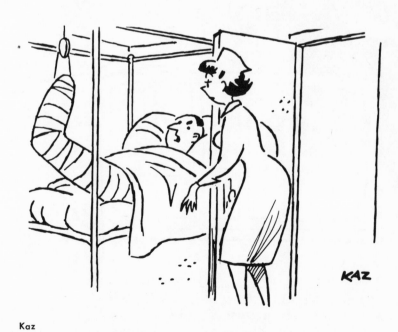

Kaz

"I slipped on a 'welcome' mat."

Tobin

"Let's simplify matters, madam. Suppose you give me *your* diagnosis first."

Lundberg   Farm Journal

**"Well, well, well—I see it's a boy
at last for the Gibsons."**

Tobey   Collier's

**"You'd feel pretty funny, Brogan, if all of a sudden
I isolated the cold germ."**

Ketcham   Saturday Evening Post

"You're fine, thanks, doctor. How am I?"

Lariar

"How long does it have to perc before it's ready, doctor?"

Sharp

"It started with a splinter three weeks ago, doc!"

Lepper   American

"I'll never make a railroad man out of him. He's
ten minutes late."

Tyrell

"Good-by, and thanks so much for the fruit you brought."

Keller   Saturday Evening Post

"Did you ever notice how some people glare at us?"

Syverson   Saturday Evening Post

"Gad! I wish you could see this!"

Roth   Saturday Evening Post

"Oh, sure I clean and dust and wash the dishes and make the bed—though not as often as you did, of course!"

Keate   Saturday Evening Post

"Worst damn Napoleon complex I've ever seen!"

Williams

Collier's

"Sorry, but I'm the only one on duty today."

Roth

Women's Home Companion

"What'll I tell your mother? She wanted a girl!"

Ericson

The Physician

Wilkinson

Saturday Evening Post

Corka   Argosy

Marcus   Saturday Evening Post

**"Would you mind going to the medical convention
with me this week, all expenses paid?"**

Salo

Saturday Evening Post

"It's fun hearing them propose, even though they're delirious."

Dennis

"He said: 'We'll operate today at four, Mr. Eggbert.' I'm *not* Eggbert! My name is Finklefinger!"

Locke

Collier's

"It's a father! I'm a girl! I'm a girl!"

Scott Brown   Saturday Evening Post

"... and then we made it here eight miles in seven
minutes. That was about six hours ago."

Dennis

"One of John's greatest disappointments was when
he flunked out in pre-med school."

Marcus   Saturday Evening Post

**"Better hurry up and get well, Flinthall. Your
vacation starts tomorrow."**

Gibson   This Week

"We won't take our medicine. Shall I get tough?"

Wilkinson

Saturday Evening Post

"I'd say offhand he has a fever!"

Dennis

Monahan   Saturday Evening Post

"Hiccups still bothering you, Mr. Blake?"

Wilkinson   Halt

**"All that I know is that the ticket broker said they
were front row seats to an opening!"**

MATERNITY WARD

1.

2.

3.

4.

5.

6.

Boltinoff   Collier's

"Congratulations, it's a *girl!*"

7.

8.

Salo

Saturday Evening Post

"How are the children and my good dishes?"

Ross

**"He's a cab driver, doctor, and this is
the only thing that keeps him quiet."**

Roir   PM

"... and no more meals. You're getting enough
between meals!"

Stamaty   Collier's

"The college of surgery wants one who still has
her appendix."

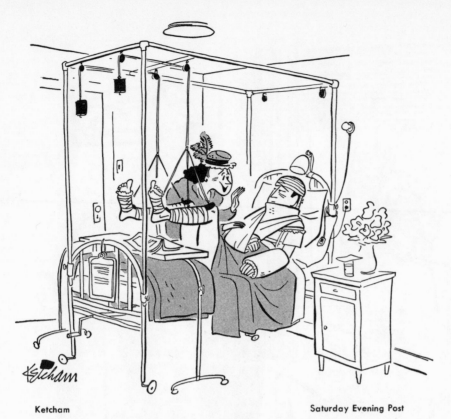

Ketcham

Saturday Evening Post

"I've got wonderful news for you, dear! Your lawyer said you had the right of way!"

Kaz

"Wouldn't you think new fathers would be more interested in their kids?"

Helle   Household

"We can do without your practical jokes, Miss Willis."

Baeb   Saturday Evening Post

**"I brought you something to while away the lonely
hours, Anderson."**

Kaz

**"Good heavens! He got out of the wrong side of the
bed this morning!"**

Lepper   Collier's

**"That's Dr. Jamison showing off his candid
X rays again!"**

Price   Saturday Evening Post

"Good night! A full house!"

Garel   Collier's

"Bill, go downstairs to the phone booth, call this place, ask them how I'm doing and come back and tell me, will ya?"

Hilton   Collier's

"I'd love to go to the movies with you, Gerald, but I can't get a baby sitter."

Sharp

"Hello, Diathermy Ward? Are my frankfurters cooked yet?"

Johns

Saturday Evening Post

"Let me put it this way . . . if you were a building
you'd be condemned."

Matthews

Collier's

"I hope I'll get to the root of your trouble, Mr. Brown,
because I've had the same thing myself for years."

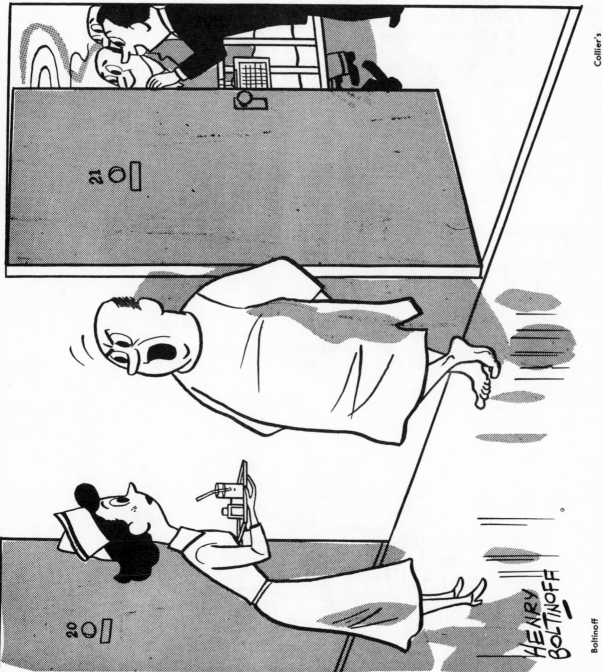

"There's such a mob in there visiting me, I had to come out for a breath of fresh air!"

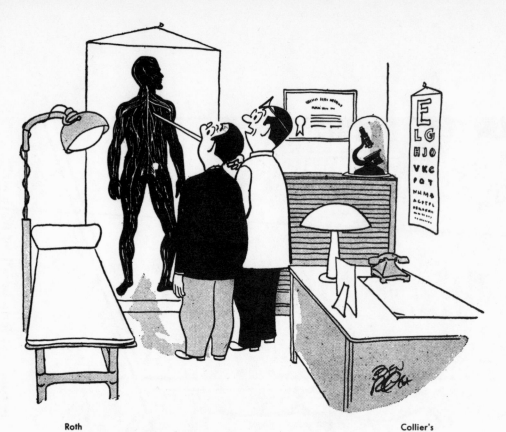

Roth   Collier's

"Hampton Road runs along here, and then you turn
off into Craig Avenue, drive along Park Place, turn
right, and there is my home."

Marquez   American Legion Magazine

"Help, somebody!!"

Rayon

"Try to get here in about an hour, Grace—I'll have so much to tell you."

Tobin   Collier's

"He'll feel better now. I just told him he's too sick to
go to school."

Roth   Saturday Evening Post

"You have tonsilitis complicated by that $109.00
you've owed me for two years!"

Hoifield

"**Don't worry about a thing. Everyone at the office is going to pitch in and do your work as soon as we can find out what you were doing.**"

"What you have is a common cold, and there is no known cure for it. But cheer up—it may run into pneumonia—and we know what to do for that!"

Kenik   Saturday Evening Post

"I'm sure we'll get some sort of reaction this time."

Cramer

Bo Brown   Collier's

"Want me to take a stab at it?"

Townsend   Cigar and Tobacco Journal

**"Have a father, I just became the baby of a seven
pound cigar."**

Gibson   This Week

"But that's as smooth as I can get it with the patient in there!"

Cavalli

Saturday Evening Post

"I sure miss you, mom . . . I haven't been seeing much of pop, either."

Sharp

"While waiting for a patient, suppose I trim your moustache!"

Tobin

American

"She's a practical nurse—she only nurses rich old men."

Roth

Saturday Evening Post

"Imagine us—founding a dynasty!"

Kaz

". . . and divide by two!"

Fox

"I'll have you out of here in a week—one way or the other."

"Of course, my *secret* ambition is to be a surgeon."

"Are the nurses treating you all right, Mr. Miller?"

Tobey

Saturday Evening Post

"He called up and wants to know what you intend doing about
his fender."

Lariar   Saturday Evening Post

"Cut Private Tucker's vitamins 50%, Miss Parks!"

Fine   Saturday Evening Post

**"The neighbors have been so kind and understanding—
Mr. Beemer got right out and put rock salt on his walk."**

Scott Brown   Collier's

"The reason we need a loan is we're expecting a baby. Incidently, our need
for it is rather urgent. Matter of fact, we're on our way to the hospital now."

Frick   True Detective

**"Well, old man, we've finally gotten to the seat of your trouble.
You're sick."**

Hagglund

"Call the newspapers!—Get a wire out to the nation wide radio hookups!—Contact the local radio and television stations!—Notify the President!—"

Diamond

American

"Don't bother getting up, Mr. Tompkins."

Taber   Saturday Evening Post

"AHHHH!"

Dempsey   Collier's

**"I'll bet *she* has no trouble waking you up in
the morning."**

Lariar

Collier's

"... And you always tell the patient it was the worst looking appendix you ever took out!"

Sibley   Saturday Evening Post

"Before I see the doctor—there's something I'd like to find out."

Marquez   Saturday Evening Post

"Now don't you worry about anything at home, dear; everybody is just wonderful about charging things!"

Ross

"Don't move, dear! I'm getting an idea for a new hat!"

"Hurt?"

Harrison

1000 Jokes

Kaz

ACKNOWLEDGMENTS

THE EDITOR wishes to thank the following contributing cartoonists for their kind cooperation:

Bo Brown, Boltinoff, Mack, Sharp, O'Brien, Taber, Millar, Marquez, Rayon, Whiting, Gibson, Goldstein, Tyrrell, Scott Brown, Lundberg, Salo, McCormick, Trachtenberg, Price, Syverson, Boserman, Quinn, Rodriguez, Roir, Corka, Dempsey, Ketcham, Marcus, Locke, Schroeter, Paplow, Bernhardt, Dennis, Pearson, Keate, Ross, LaMendola, Ridgeway, Ericson, Wolfe, Jane King, Kaz, Tobin, Tobey, Lepper, Keller, Roth, Williams, Wilkinson, Locke, Monahan, Stamaty, Helle, Baeb, Garel, Hilton, Johns, Matthews, Oakes, Hoifjeld, Cramer, Kenik, Townsend, Cavalli, Fox, Henrikson, Hagglund, Diamond, Fine, Harrison, O'Neal, Sibley, Frick.

To the following magazines, my thanks for permission to reprint: *The Saturday Evening Post, Collier's, The American, This Week, Saturday Review of Literature, Liberty, George Matthew Adams Service, True Detective, Woman's Home Companion, Argosy, The Physician, American Legion, 1000 Jokes, Cigar and Tobacco Journal, P.M., Farm Journal, Judge, Current Medical Digest, Household,* and *Halt*.

In every case, the editor has been scrupulously careful to contact owners of copyright, and believes that no available permission has escaped him. If he has unwittingly offended against any interests, necessary apologies and acknowledgments will be made.